CONTENTS

Ben

Callum

11

16

19

24

29

ABOUT THE AUTHOR

As a child, Scott Nickel wanted to be a comic book writer or a mad scientist. Now he gets to do both. In his secret literary lab, Scott has created more than a dozen graphic novels featuring time travellers, zombies, robots, giant insects, and mutant dinner ladies. Scott's *Night of the Homework Zombies* received the 2007 Golden Duck award for Best Science Fiction Picture Book. When not creating his own crazy comics, Scott squeezes in a full-time job as a writer and editor of Garfield comic books.

ABOUT THE ILLUSTRATOR

Steve Harpster has loved drawing funny cartoons, mean monsters, and goofy gadgets ever since he was able to pick up a pencil. When he was in Year 2 at school, he was able to avoid his writing projects by working on the pictures for stories instead. Steve got a job drawing funny pictures for books, and that's really what he's best at!

GLOSSARY

brachiosaur long-necked, plant-eating dinosaur that lived more than 150 million years ago

carnivore meat-eater, like a T. rex or your dog

dino droppings prehistoric poo. Scientists call fossilized dinosaur poo "coprolites".

eek the proper sound to make when you are frightened by the mark you've got for your history test; "argh" will also work.

geek anyone who knows more about computers and science than you do

Ultra Galactic the master, or highest, level on the Space Slime Commandos video game

zillionth a lot! More than a jillion, but not as much as a gazillion.

You'll be tested on these words, so pay attention!

DINO FACTS

You can tell a plant-eating dinosaur from a meat-eater by noting how many legs they walked on. Plant-eaters usually stomped around on all four legs. Swift and deadly meat-eaters hunted on two legs.

Brachiosaurus had nostrils on the top of its head. Some scientists think the placement of its nose, and its large nasal cavity, gave this plant-eater a strong sense of smell.

Pteranodon flew over the vast prehistoric oceans, diving into the water to snatch fish. Some scientists think that when this flying creature was tired, it sat on the waves, bobbing up and down like a cork or a duck. A really **big** duck.

Tyrannosaurus rex had a mouthful of deadly teeth, which were shaped like bananas. But why did he have such puny arms? Dino experts think the tiny paws might mean that *T. rex* didn't fight for its food but ate creatures that were already dead. Yuck!

At least one *T. rex* has left its *poo* behind. Scientists examined the fossilized dung and found bone fragments from a *Triceratops*. There's no way of knowing whether this three-horned dino was alive or dead at the time of the meal.

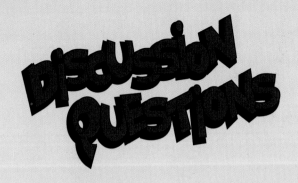

DISCUSSION QUESTIONS

1.) If time machines really existed, would you use one to go back in time to retake a test? Do you think that would be fair?

2.) In books and films, whenever humans and dinosaurs get together, the dinosaurs attack the titchy humans. Do you think this would really happen?

3.) If dinosaurs were sold in your local pet shop, which one would you want to take home, and why? How do you think your parents or friends would react to your new pet?

WRITING PROMPTS

1.) Everyone makes mistakes. If you could go back to a time when you made one of your past mistakes, which mistake would you choose? Write about how you would fix it.

2.) David's geeky brother, Callum, celebrated the invention of his time pod by making a giant egg mayo sandwich. If you were famous for creating an invention, write about what it would be. How would you celebrate?

3.) At a nearby shopping centre, a time pod will be set up for willing customers. You can travel back to prehistoric times and see dinosaurs up close and personal. You can take three items along on your trip, but only three. Write about which ones you would take, and why.

FIND OUT MORE

Books

Dinosaur Encyclopedia, Caroline Bingham
  (Dorling Kindersley, 2007)

Prehistoric Scary Creatures, John Malam
  (Book House, 2008)

Website

Visit the Natural History Museum's website to find information on more than 300 types of dinosaur, play dinosaur games, and find out what sort of dinosaur you would be!

www.nhm.ac.uk/kids-only/dinosaurs